Skills Practice

KS2
Success

10-MINUTE TESTS

Maths

Paul Broadbent

Sample page

clear instructional text   topic being covered   test number for quick reference

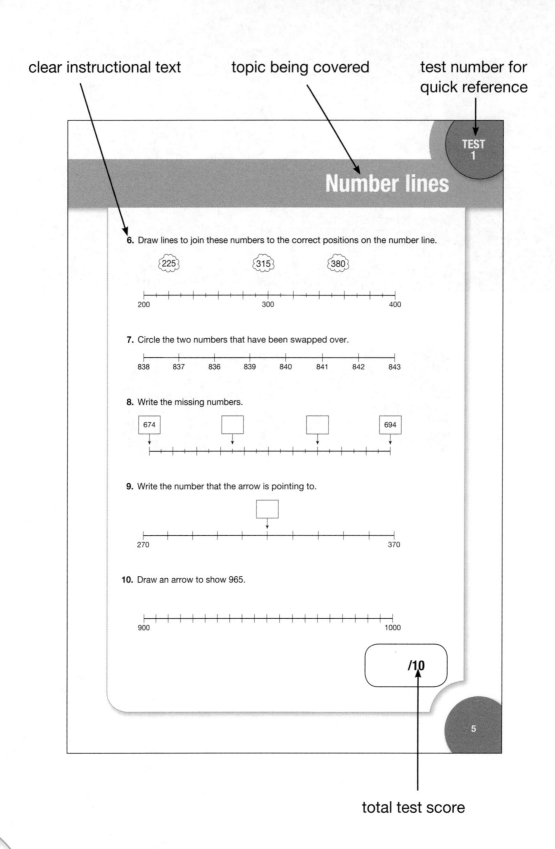

TEST 1

Number lines

6. Draw lines to join these numbers to the correct positions on the number line.

225   315   380

200   300   400

7. Circle the two numbers that have been swapped over.

838 837 836 839 840 841 842 843

8. Write the missing numbers.

674   694

9. Write the number that the arrow is pointing to.

270   370

10. Draw an arrow to show 965.

900   1000

/10

5

total test score

2

Contents

Number lines

1. Write the missing numbers on the number line.

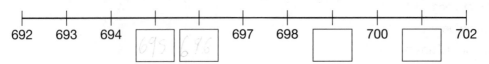

692   693   694   [695] [696]   697   698   [ ]   700   [ ]   702

2. Write the number that each arrow is pointing to.

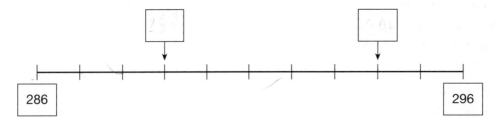

286   296

3. Draw an arrow to show 565.

500   600

4. Write the missing number.

740   [733]   760

5. Circle the even numbers.

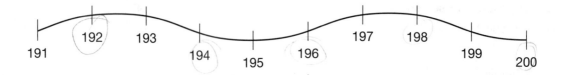

191   192   193   194   195   196   197   198   199   200

Number lines

6. Draw lines to join these numbers to the correct positions on the number line.

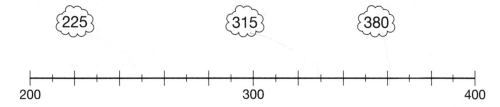

225   315   380

200   300   400

7. Circle the two numbers that have been swapped over.

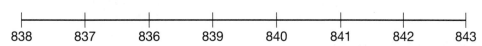

838   837   836   839   840   841   842   843

8. Write the missing numbers.

674   694

9. Write the number that the arrow is pointing to.

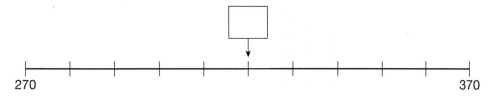

270   370

10. Draw an arrow to show 965.

900   1000

/10

Place value

1. Write the missing numbers.

a)

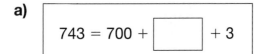

743 = 700 + [   ] + 3

b)

819 = [   ] + 10 + [   ]

2. Put a circle around the largest number below.

466   480   409   489   471

3. Write these numbers using digits.

a) one hundred and forty-three ➔ [   ]

b) six hundred and eight   ➔ [   ]

4. Write the number shown on this abacus. [   ]

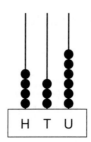

H T U

5. Draw the beads on this abacus to show the number 615.

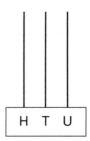

H T U

Place value

6. Write these in hundreds, tens and units (ones).

a) 527 = ☐ + ☐ + ☐

b) 816 = ☐ + ☐ + ☐

7. Answer these.

a) 84 × 10 = _____

b) 6 × 100 = _____

8. Write these numbers as words.

a) 470 → _____

b) 904 → _____

9. What number is 10 times smaller than 510?

_____

10. What number does this show?

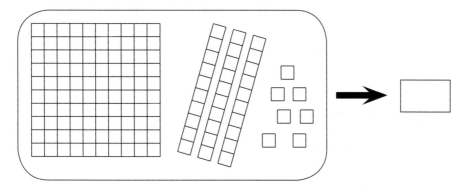

/10

Ordering numbers

1. Circle the smallest number in each pair.

a)
| 184   149 |

b)
| 306   360 |

c)
| 799   801 |

2. Write these numbers in order, starting with the smallest.

     870

_____   _____   _____   _____   _____

3. Write any whole number that is between 458 and 462.

_____

4. Tick the largest amount in this set.

| 754 g | | 399 g | | 790 g | | 739 g |

☐   ☐   ☐   ☐

5. These numbers should be in order.

Colour the two numbers that have been swapped.

914 — 915 — 919 — 917 — 918 — 916

Ordering numbers

6. I am thinking of a whole number. It is greater than 748 and less than 750.

What number am I thinking of? _____

7. Circle the largest number in each pair.

a)

| 614 | 461 |

b)

| 299 | 276 |

c)

| 809 | 890 |

8. Write these lengths in order, starting with the shortest.

845 cm   659 cm   700 cm   694 cm   657 cm

_____   _____   _____   _____   _____

9. Write a number in each box so that the numbers are in size order.

508   [ ]   552   571   [ ]   593

10. Write any whole number that is greater than 898 and less than 902.

_____

/10

Rounding numbers

1. Round these numbers to the nearest 10.

2. Join these numbers to the nearest 10.

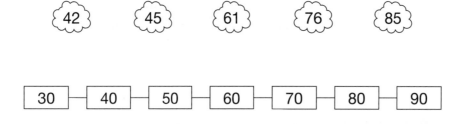

3. Write two numbers that would round to 130 to the nearest 10.

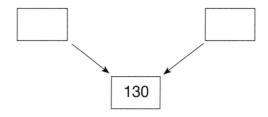

4. Round these numbers to the nearest 10.

5. Read this scale to the nearest 10 g.

Rounding numbers

6. Round these numbers to the nearest 100.

   a) 368 → ☐   **b)** 549 → ☐

7. Read this scale to the nearest 100 g.

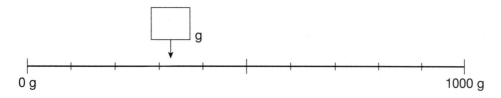

8. Join these numbers to the nearest 100.

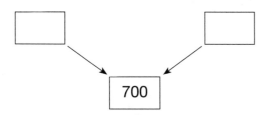

  452   620   681   760

| 400 | 500 | 600 | 700 | 800 |

9. Write two numbers that would round to 700 to the nearest hundred.

  ☐   ☐

       700

10. Round these to the nearest hundred metres.

   a) 352 m → ☐ m   **b)** 738 m → ☐ m

/10

Number sequences

1. Write the missing numbers.

2. Write the next three numbers in this sequence.

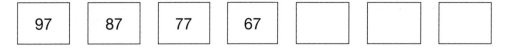

| 97 | 87 | 77 | 67 | | | |

3. Draw the jumps and continue the number sequence.

4. Colour the even numbers.

5. Write the missing numbers.

Number sequences

6. Write the missing numbers.

78   82   [   ]   [   ]   94   [   ]   102

7. Draw the jumps and continue the number sequence.

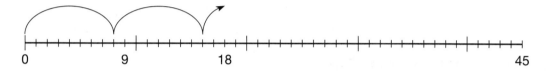

0   9   18   45

8. Circle the odd numbers.

| 353 | 354 | 355 | 356 | 357 | 358 | 359 |

9. Write the missing numbers.

20   26
    23   29

10. Write the next three numbers in this sequence.

277 — 275 — 273 — 271 — [ ] — [ ] — [ ]

/10

Fractions

1. Tick the shape that is divided into quarters.

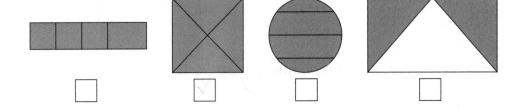

☐   ☑   ☐   ☐

2. Colour $\frac{2}{3}$ of each of these shapes.

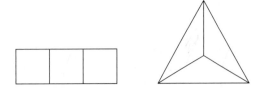

3. What is $\frac{1}{10}$ of £30?

£ _____

4. Write the fraction shown by each of these shapes.

a)

b)

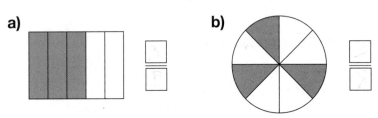

5. $\frac{1}{4}$ of 16 = ☐

Fractions

6. What must be added to each of these fractions to make one whole?

a) $\frac{1}{2} + \frac{\square}{\square} = 1$

b) $\frac{1}{4} + \frac{\square}{\square} = 1$

7. What is $\frac{1}{3}$ of 15?

_____

8. Colour these shapes to show the fractions.

a) 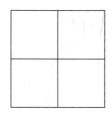 $\frac{3}{4}$

b)  $\frac{1}{6}$

9. $\frac{1}{5}$ of 20 = $\square$

10. Write the fraction shown by each of these.

a)

b)

/10

Equivalent fractions

Write each fraction shaded in two ways.

1.

$$\frac{1}{3} = \frac{\square}{\square}$$

2.

$$\frac{1}{4} = \frac{\square}{8}$$

3.

$$\frac{1}{2} = \frac{6}{12}$$

4.

$$\frac{1}{4} = \frac{\square}{\square}$$

5.

$$\frac{1}{2} = \frac{\square}{\square}$$

Equivalent fractions

6. Colour each fraction to make it equivalent to $\frac{1}{2}$.
   Write the fraction shown.

   a)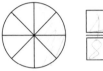

   b)

7. Colour each fraction to make it equivalent to $\frac{1}{4}$.
   Write the fraction shown.

   a)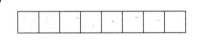

   b)

Write the equivalent fractions to these.

8. $\frac{2}{6} = \frac{\boxed{}}{\boxed{}}$

9. $\frac{4}{8} = \frac{\boxed{}}{\boxed{}}$

10.  $\frac{2}{4} = \frac{\boxed{}}{\boxed{}}$

/10

Addition and subtraction facts

1. Write the missing numbers.

a)   7 + ☐ = 15

b)   ☐ + 9 = 13

2. Answer these.

a)   14 − 8 = ☐

b)   13 + 6 = ☐

c)   18 − 7 = ☐

3. Complete these addition grids.

a)

+	8	3	5
9			
12			
5			

b)

+	12	13	14
6			
4			
3			

4. What is the difference between each pair?

a) 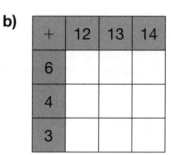 7   13 → _____

b) 8   12 → _____

c) 11   19 → _____

5. What is the total of 5, 7 and 8?

_____

Addition and subtraction facts

6. Write the missing numbers.

a) 15 − ☐ = 9

b) ☐ − 8 = 8

7. This is a **+7** machine. Write the missing numbers in the table.

IN	5		9		6	
OUT	12	18		11		20

8. This is a **−8** machine. Write the missing numbers in the table.

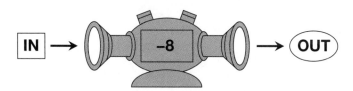

IN	14	11		17		19
OUT	6		4		5	

9. Answer these.

a) 90 − 60 = ☐

b) 40 + 30 = ☐

c) 70 − 20 = ☐

10. I am thinking of a number. If I add 8 to it, the answer is 20.

What number am I thinking of? _____

/10

Multiplication and division facts

1. Answer these.

a) $4 \times 6 =$ ◻

b) $3 \times 5 =$ ◻

c) $10 \times 7 =$ ◻

2. Answer these.

a) $18 \div 3 =$ ◻

b) $25 \div 5 =$ ◻

c) $36 \div 4 =$ ◻

3. Write four different facts for each number.

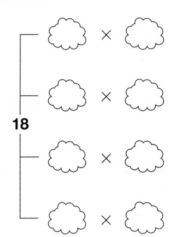

12

18

4. Which number between 20 and 30 can be divided exactly by both 3 and 4?

_____

5. Complete this multiplication grid.

×	4	7	8
3			
4			
5			

Multiplication and division facts

6. Complete each table.

 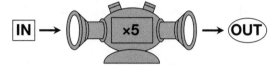

IN	4		7		10
OUT		20		36	

IN	3		6		9
OUT		25		35	

7. Write the missing numbers.

a) 8 × ☐ = 16   **b)** ☐ × 6 = 42   **c)** 3 × ☐ = 27

8. Write four different facts for each number.

24

◯ × ◯

◯ × ◯

◯ × ◯

◯ × ◯

30

◯ × ◯

◯ × ◯

◯ × ◯

◯ × ◯

9. I am thinking of a number. If I multiply it by 5, the answer is 45.

What number am I thinking of? _____

10. I am thinking of a number. If I divide it by 3, the answer is 6.

What number am I thinking of? _____

/10

Addition

1. Answer these.

    a)   56 + 30 = ☐   **b)**   74 + 80 = ☐   **c)**   38 + 90 = ☐

2. Join pairs of numbers that total 100.

    87   63   37

        46   13   54

3. Write the missing numbers.

    a)   42 + ☐ = 75   **b)**   ☐ + 34 = 96

4. What is 29 more than 52?

    _____

5. Look at these four numbers.

    | 43 | | 39 |

       | 51 | | 26 |

    Which two numbers total 82?

    _____ and _____

Addition

6. Write the missing numbers.

a) $74 + \boxed{} = 110$

b) $\boxed{} + 86 = 130$

7. Answer these.

a)
$$\begin{array}{r} 1\,4\,7 \\ +\ \ 9\,6 \\ \hline \end{array}$$

b)
$$\begin{array}{r} 2\,3\,8 \\ +\ \ 7\,7 \\ \hline \end{array}$$

c)
$$\begin{array}{r} 1\,8\,4 \\ +\ \ 5\,9 \\ \hline \end{array}$$

8. What is the total of 37, 38 and 39?

_____

9. Write the missing digits.

a)
$$\begin{array}{r} 2\ 5\ \boxed{} \\ +\ \ \ 4\ \ 9 \\ \hline \boxed{}\ 0\ 2 \end{array}$$

b)
$$\begin{array}{r} 4\ \boxed{}\ 9 \\ +\ \ \ 5\ \ 4 \\ \hline 4\ 6\ \boxed{} \end{array}$$

10. The sum of two numbers is 150. If one of the numbers is 97, what is the other number?

_____

/10

Subtraction

1. Write the difference between these numbers.

   a)

   | 48 | | | | 61 |

   b)

   | 59 | | | | 62 |

2. Answer these.

   a) 64 − 56 = ☐   **b)** 92 − 88 = ☐

3. Complete this subtraction chain.

   (60) − 19 ⟶ ☐ − 19 ⟶ ☐ − 19 ⟶ ☐

4. I am thinking of a number. If I subtract 25 from it, the answer is 64.

   What number am I thinking of? _____

5. Write the missing numbers.

   a) 72 − ☐ = 4   **b)** ☐ − 9 = 53

   c) ☐ − 8 = 39   **d)** 65 − ☐ = 7

Subtraction

6. Answer these.

a)   7 3
  − 2 6
  ‾‾‾‾‾

b)   4 8
  − 1 9
  ‾‾‾‾‾

c)   8 1
  − 3 7
  ‾‾‾‾‾

7. What is the difference between these three numbers? Fill in the boxes.

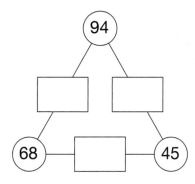

8. How much greater is 91 than 19?

_____

9. Write the missing digits.

a)   6 ☐
  − 3 8
  ‾‾‾‾‾‾
   3 1

b)   9 2
  − 4 ☐
  ‾‾‾‾‾‾
   4 6

c) ☐ 3
  − 5 8
  ‾‾‾‾‾‾
   2 5

10. The difference between two numbers is 55. If the larger number is 81, what is the other number?

_____

/10

Multiplication

1. Answer these.

a) 17 × 10 = [ ]

b) 9 × 100 = [ ]

2. Write the numbers coming out of this doubling machine.

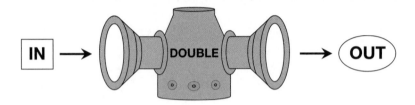

IN	15	18	32	27	43	39
OUT	30					

3. I am thinking of a number. When I multiply it by 3, the answer is 45.

What number am I thinking of?

_____

4. Answer these.

a) 19 × 4 = [ ]

b) 17 × 5 = [ ]

5. Write the missing numbers.

a) 34 × [ ] = 3400

b) [ ] × 100 = 4700

Multiplication

6. Answer these.

a)   2 3
      × 4
    _____

b)   3 1
      × 5
    _____

c)   4 5
      × 3
    _____

7. A hall has 38 rows of chairs. If there are 10 chairs in each row, how many chairs are there altogether?

_____

8. Mrs Patel drives 57 km to work and drives home the same distance at the end of the day.

How far does she drive altogether?

_____ km

9. Write the missing digits.

a)   3   7
      ×   ☐
    _____
      1 1 1

b)   4   ☐
      ×   5
    _____
      2 2 0

c)   ☐   2
      ×   4
    _____
      2 4 8

10. What number is double 88?

_____

/10

Division

1. Halve each number and write the answer.

a)  **b)** 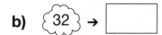 **c)**

2. Complete each table.

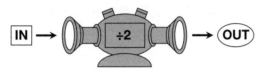 

IN	16	8	22	36	80
OUT					

IN	40	20	25	80	45
OUT					

3. How many threes are there in 18?

☆ ☆ ☆ ☆ ☆ ☆

☆ ☆ ☆ ☆ ☆ ☆

☆ ☆ ☆ ☆ ☆ ☆ _____

4. Answer these.

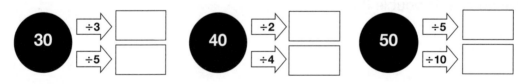

5. 25 plums are shared equally between four bags.

a) How many plums are in each bag? _____

b) How many plums are left over? _____

6. Answer these.

a) 24 ÷ 3 = ☐

b) 38 ÷ 2 = ☐

c) 55 ÷ 5 = ☐

7. Complete each table.

IN	36	42	18	24	27
OUT					

IN	36	16	24	32	40
OUT					

8. What is the remainder when 20 is divided by 3?

_____

9. Answer these.

a) 14 ÷ 4 = ☐ r ☐

b) 37 ÷ 4 = ☐ r ☐

10. A box holds three table tennis balls. How many boxes are needed for 17 balls?

_____

/10

Money

1. Write the total amount for each of these.

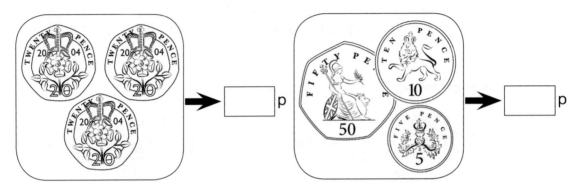

2. What is the change from 50p for this amount?

Change from 50p = ☐ p

3. What is the fewest number of coins to make exactly 58p? _____

4. Look at the coins below. How much more is needed to make £5? _____

5. Use five coins to make 94p. Write the amount on each coin.

Answer booklet: Maths 10-Minute Tests, age 7–8

Test 1
1. 695, 696, 699, 701
2. 289, 294
3. Check arrow is at 565.
4. 754
5. 192, 194, 196, 198, 200
6. Check numbers are at correct position.
7. 838, 836
8. 681, 688
9. 320
10. Check arrow is at 965.

Test 2
1. a) 40   b) 800, 9
2. 489
3. a) 143   b) 608
4. 436
5.

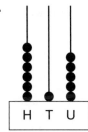

H T U

6. a) 500 + 20 + 7
   b) 800 + 10 + 6
7. a) 840   b) 600
8. a) four hundred and seventy
   b) nine hundred and four
9. 51
10. 137

Test 3
1. a) 149   b) 306
   c) 799
2. 178, 718, 780, 807, 870
3. One number: 459, 460 or 461
4. 790 g
5. 919, 916
6. 749
7. a) 614   b) 299
   c) 890
8. 657 cm, 659 cm, 694 cm, 700 cm, 845 cm
9. Check the first number is between 508 and 552, and the second number is between 571 and 593.
10. One number: 899, 900 or 901

Test 4
1. 70, 90
2. 42 ➜ 40, 45 ➜ 50, 61 ➜ 60, 76 ➜ 80, 85 ➜ 90
3. Any two numbers from 125 to 134.
4. 150, 280
5. 70 g
6. a) 400   b) 500
7. 300 g
8. 452 ➜ 500, 620 ➜ 600, 681 ➜ 700, 760 ➜ 800
9. Any two numbers from 650 to 749.
10. a) 400 m   b) 700 m

Test 5
1. 25, 30, 35, 40, 45, 50
2. 57, 47, 37
3. Check jumps at 9, 12, 15, 18, 21, 24, 27, 30.
4. 148, 146, 144
5. 90, 82, 80
6. 86, 90, 98
7. Check jumps at 24, 32, 40.
8. 353, 355, 357, 359
9. 32, 35, 38, 41, 44, 47
10. 269, 267, 265

Test 6
1. The second shape should be ticked (square).
2. Check that two parts of each shape have been shaded.
3. £3
4. a) $\frac{3}{5}$ b) $\frac{3}{8}$
5. 4
6. a) $\frac{1}{2}$ b) $\frac{3}{4}$
7. 5
8. a) Check that three parts of the shape have been shaded.
   b) Check that one part of the shape has been shaded.
9. 4
10. a) $\frac{5}{6}$ b) $\frac{2}{3}$

Test 7
1. $\frac{1}{3} = \frac{3}{9}$
2. $\frac{1}{4} = \frac{2}{8}$
3. $\frac{1}{2} = \frac{6}{12}$
4. $\frac{1}{4} = \frac{3}{12}$
5. $\frac{1}{3} = \frac{2}{6}$
6. a) $\frac{4}{8}$ b) $\frac{3}{6}$
7. a) $\frac{2}{8}$ b) $\frac{3}{12}$
8. $\frac{1}{3}$
9. $\frac{1}{2}$
10. $\frac{1}{2}$

Test 8
1. a) 8   b) 4
2. a) 6   b) 19
   c) 11
3. a)

+	8	3	5
9	17	12	14
12	20	15	17
5	13	8	10

b)

+	12	13	14
6	18	19	20
4	16	17	18
3	15	16	17

4. a) 6   b) 4   c) 8
5. 20
6. a) 6   b) 16
7.

IN	5	11	9	4	6	13
OUT	12	18	16	11	13	20

8.

IN	14	11	12	17	13	19
OUT	6	3	4	9	5	11

9. a) 30   b) 70   c) 50
10. 12

Test 9
1. a) 24   b) 15   c) 70
2. a) 6   b) 5   c) 9
3. Any four facts for each number:
   12 ➜ 2 × 6, 6 × 2, 3 × 4, 4 × 3, 1 × 12, 12 × 1
   18 ➜ 1 × 18, 18 × 1, 2 × 9, 9 × 2, 3 × 6, 6 × 3

1

4. 24

5.

×	4	7	8
3	12	21	24
4	16	28	32
5	20	35	40

6.

IN	4	5	7	9	10
OUT	16	20	28	36	40

IN	3	5	6	7	9
OUT	15	25	30	35	45

7. a) 2 **b)** 7 **c)** 9

8. Any four facts for each number:
24 → 1 × 24, 24 × 1,
    2 × 12, 12 × 2, 3 × 8,
    8 × 3, 4 × 6, 6 × 4
30 → 1 × 30, 30 × 1,
    2 × 15, 15 × 2, 3 × 10,
    10 × 3, 5 × 6, 6 × 5

9. 9

10. 18

Test 10

1. a) 86 **b)** 154
   c) 128

2. 63 + 37, 46 + 54, 87 + 13

3. a) 33 **b)** 62

4. 81

5. 39 and 43

6. a) 36 **b)** 44

7. a) 243 **b)** 315
   c) 243

8. 114

9. a) 253 + 49 = 302
   b) 409 + 54 = 463

10. 53

Test 11

1. a) 13 **b)** 3

2. a) 8 **b)** 4

3. 41, 22, 3

4. 89

5. a) 68 **b)** 62
   c) 47 **d)** 58

6. a) 47 **b)** 29 **c)** 44

7.

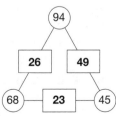

8. 72

9. a) 9 **b)** 6 **c)** 8

10. 26

Test 12

1. a) 170 **b)** 900

2.

IN	15	18	32	27	43	39
OUT	30	36	64	54	86	78

3. 15

4. a) 76 **b)** 85

5. a) 100 **b)** 47

6. a) 92 **b)** 155 **c)** 135

7. 380

8. 114 km

9. a) 3 **b)** 4 **c)** 6

10. 176

Test 13

1. a) 9 **b)** 16 **c)** 25

2.

IN	16	8	22	36	80
OUT	8	4	11	18	40

IN	40	20	25	80	45
OUT	8	4	5	16	9

3. 6

4. 30 → 10, 6
   40 → 20, 10
   50 → 10, 5

5. a) 6
   b) 1

6. a) 8 **b)** 19 **c)** 11

7.

IN	36	42	18	24	27
OUT	12	14	6	8	9

IN	36	16	24	32	40
OUT	9	4	6	8	10

8. 2

9. a) 3 r 2 **b)** 9 r 1

10. 6

Test 14

1. 60p, 65p

2. 8p

3. 4 coins (50p, 5p, 2p 1p)

4. £2

5. 50p, 20p, 20p, 2p, 2p coins

6. 70p

7. 15p

8. £2, 50p, 10p, 5p, 2p coins

9. £6.50

10. 450p = £4.50

Test 15

1. Total 12 → 3, 3 and 3, 3 or
     2, 2 and 2, 6 or
     4, 4, and 4, 0

2. Total 7 → 2, 2 and 2, 1 or
     1, 1 and 1, 4

3. Total 9 → 1, 1, and 1, 6 or
     2, 2, and 2, 3 or
     3, 3 and 3, 0

4. Total 16 → 4, 4 and 4, 4 or
     5, 5 and 5, 1

5. Total 17 → 4, 4, and 4, 5 or
     5, 5 and 5, 2

6. Total 15 → 3, 3, and 3, 6 or
     4, 4 and 4, 3 or
     5, 5 and 5, 0

7. Total 23 → 6, 6 and 6, 5

Test 16

Check faces are copied accurately.

Test 17

1. 7

2. $\frac{6}{18}$ or $\frac{1}{3}$

3. 5 cm

4. $1\frac{1}{2}$, $3\frac{1}{4}$, $4\frac{3}{4}$

5. 8 quarters

6. a) 3 **b)** 8 **c)** 10

7. 1500 ml

8. 7 kg

9. $\frac{1}{3}$ of 18 litres

10. a) 10 **b)** 4
    c) 5 **d)** 2

Test 18

1. Check the pentagon (five sides) is crossed out.

2. hexagon

3. 4

4.

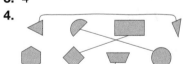

5. Check four triangles have been ticked.

6. pentagon

7. Check an isosceles triangle (two sides the same length) has been drawn.

8. square

9. Check the hexagon (six sides) is crossed out.

10. 6

Test 19
1. cone
2. false
3. The first shape should be circled.
4. pyramid
5. cuboids
6. **a)** sphere **b)** hemisphere
7. 6
8. cylinders
9. 2
10. pyramid

Test 20
1.

2.

3. E
4. Yes
5.
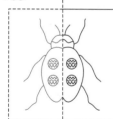

6.
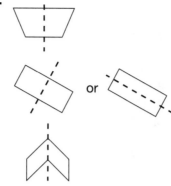
7. The 4th triangle should be crossed out.
8. W, E
9. Yes
10.
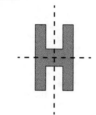
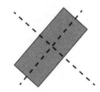

Test 21
1–5.
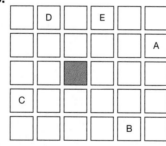
6. bench
7. see-saw
8. swing
9. see-saw
10. swing

Test 22
1. Check each right angle is ticked (2nd image, 3rd image).
2. Check a right angle (90°) has been drawn.
3. 4
4. Check each right angle is ticked (1, 2).
5. Check the largest angle is circled (3rd image).
6. 2
7. Check all right angles are ticked (6).
8. Check the smallest angle is circled (3rd image).
9. Check there is a dot at each right angle (1st, 2nd, 4th and 6th images).
10. Check the rectangle is ticked (3rd image).

Test 23
1. 200 cm
2. 1 cm, 4 cm, 9 cm
3. 8.4 or 8.5 cm
4. 120 cm
5. **a)** 55 cm **b)** 32 cm
6. 5 cm
7. **a)** 500 cm **b)** 50 cm
8. $3\frac{1}{2}$ cm, $7\frac{1}{2}$ cm, $10\frac{1}{2}$ cm
9. 2000 m
10. 150 cm

Test 24
1. 2000 ml
2. 650 ml, 850 ml
3. 10
4. 750 ml
5. 1500 ml
6. 2 litres, 1 litre
7. 5
8. 250 ml, 400 ml
9. 750 ml
10. 1500 ml

Test 25
1. 500 g
2. 5
3. $4\frac{1}{2}$ kg
4. 150 g
5. 3000 g
6. 2 kg
7. 20
8. 2500 g
9. 1 kg 500 g
10. 4500 g

Test 26

1. 5:55, 10:35
2. 11:10 a.m.
3. 31 days
4. 1:15, 7:25
5. 50 minutes
6. 45 minutes
7.

8. 3:35
9. 25 minutes
10. 30 days

Test 27

1. 12
2. Friday

3. 9
4. 3
5. 44
6. tea
7. 9
8. 9
9. milk
10. 50

Test 28

1–5.

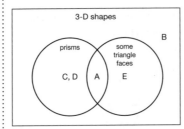

6–10.

	Can eat the skin	Cannot eat the skin
Has a stone	peach, cherry	
Does not have a stone	strawberry	pineapple, banana

Test 29

1. a) PEPAL
   b) GPRAE
   c) RECHRY
   d) GENORA
2. a) An apple should be drawn.
   b) A grape should be drawn.
   c) A cherry should be drawn.
   d) An orange should be drawn.

Test 30

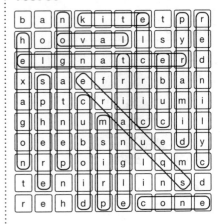

Published by Letts Educational
An imprint of HarperCollinsPublishers
77–85 Fulham Palace Road
London W6 8JB
Telephone: 0844 576 8126
Fax: 0844 576 8131
Email: education@harpercollins.co.uk
Website: www.lettsrevision.com

ISBN 9781844197231

First published in 2013

Text © Paul Broadbent

Design and illustration © 2013 Letts Educational,
an imprint of HarperCollinsPublishers

Every effort has been made to trace copyright
holders and obtain their permission for the use of
copyright material. The author and publisher will
gladly receive information enabling them to rectify
any error or omission in subsequent editions. All
facts are correct at time of going to press.

All rights reserved. No part of this publication
may be reproduced, stored in a retrieval system,
or transmitted, in any form or by any means,
electronic, mechanical, photocopying, recording
or otherwise, without the prior permission of
Letts Educational.

Money

6. What is the change from £2 for two cakes each costing 65p? _____

7. These coins were used to pay for a book costing £3.85.

What change was given? _____

8. Use five coins to make £2.67. Write the amount on each coin.

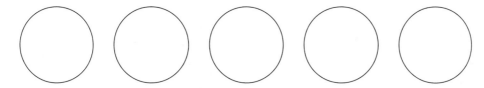

9. What is the total cost of a T-shirt costing £3.80 and shorts costing £2.70?

£ _____

10. Write this amount in two ways.

[ ] p = £ [ ]

/10

Domino pairs

This domino pair totals 10.

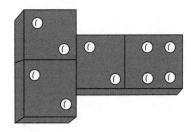

Draw spots on these dominoes.
One domino must be a double.
Touching dominoes must match.

1.

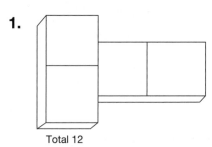

Total 12

2.

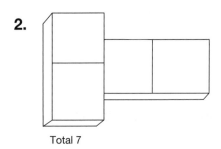

Total 7

3.

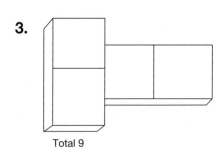

Total 9

4.

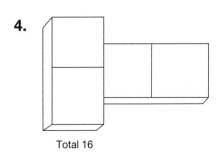

Total 16

5.

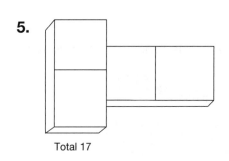

Total 17

6.

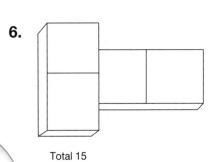

Total 15

7.

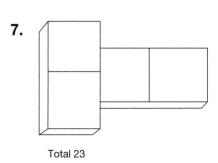

Total 23

Face fun

Copy this face onto the other grids.

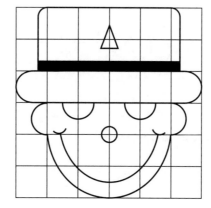

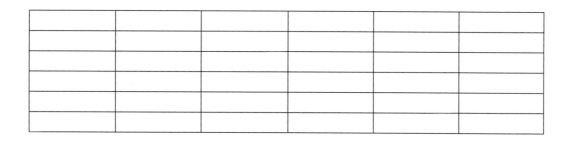

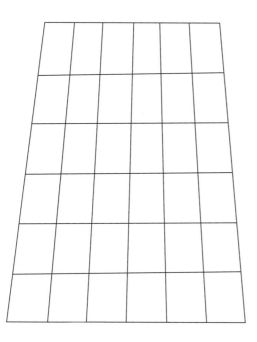

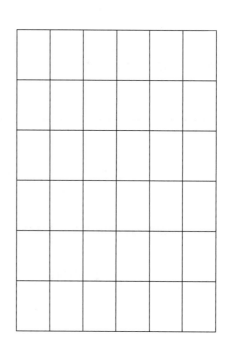

Fractions of quantities

1. Colour $\frac{1}{2}$ of these shapes.

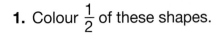

$\frac{1}{2}$ of 14 = ⬚

2. What fraction of these beads are square?

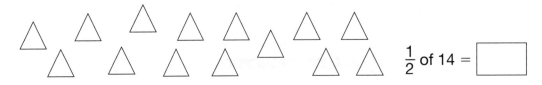

3. What is $\frac{1}{4}$ of 20 cm?

_____ cm

4. Write the fraction that each arrow points to.

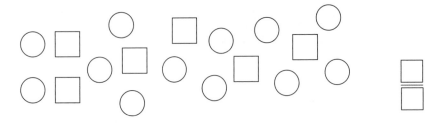

5. How many quarters are there in two wholes?

_____ quarters

Fractions of quantities

6. What is $\frac{1}{10}$ of each of these numbers?

a)   30 → [   ]　　　　　b)   80 → [   ]　　　　　c)   100 → [   ]

7. A jug holds 3 litres when it is full.

How much liquid is in the jug when it is half full?

_____ ml

8. What is $\frac{1}{4}$ of 28 kg?

_____ kg

9. Circle the largest amount.

| $\frac{1}{3}$ of 18 litres | $\frac{1}{5}$ of 25 litres |

10. Answer these.

a) $\frac{1}{2}$ of 20 = [   ]　　　　　b) $\frac{1}{5}$ of 20 = [   ]

c) $\frac{1}{4}$ of 20 = [   ]　　　　　d) $\frac{1}{10}$ of 20 = [   ]

/10

2-D shapes

1. Cross out the odd shape from this set.

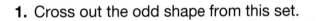

2. Name this shape.

_____

3. How many sides does a quadrilateral have?

_____

4. Draw lines to join each half shape to its matching whole shape.

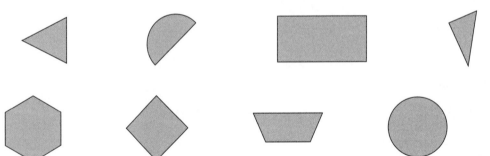

5. Tick the triangles in this set of shapes.

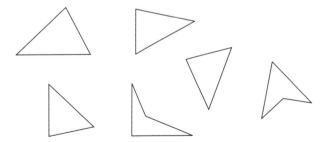

2-D shapes

6. Name this shape.

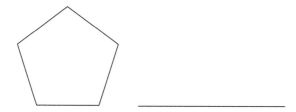

_____

7. Draw a triangle on this grid.
Make two of the sides the same length.

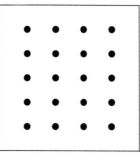

8. What shape has four equal sides and four right angles?

_____

9. Cross out the odd shape from this set.

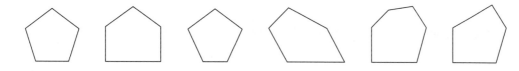

10. How many sides does a hexagon have?

_____

/10

3-D shapes

1. Name this shape.

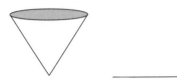

_____

2. True or false? A cuboid always has two square faces.

_____

3. Circle the odd one out from this set.

4. What is the name of the odd one out above?

_____

5. What is the name of the shapes in this set?

  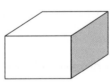

_____

3-D shapes

6. Name each of these 3-D shapes.

   a)

   b)

   _____   _____

7. How many faces does a cube have?

   _____

8. What is the name of the shapes in this set?

   _____

9. How many triangle faces does a triangular prism have?

   _____

10. Name this shape.

    _____

    /10

Symmetry

1. Draw the reflection of this shape.

2. Draw a line of reflection on each shape.

  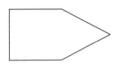

3. Tick the square that is a reflection of A.

a mirror line

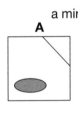 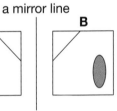   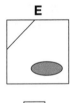

4. Is a rectangle symmetrical?   Yes / No

5. Draw the reflection of this shape.

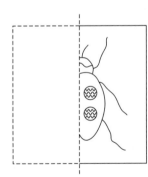

Symmetry

6. Draw one line of symmetry on each shape.

7. Cross out the triangle that is **not** symmetrical.

8. Complete these symmetrical letters.

 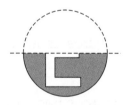

9. Is a square symmetrical?   Yes / No

10. Draw two lines of symmetry on these shapes.

/10

Movement and direction

Start from the grey square each time.

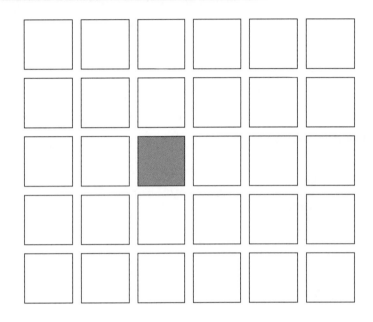

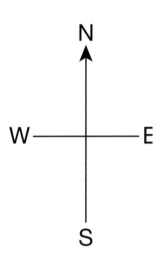

1. Go one square North, then three squares East. Write A in the box.

2. Go two squares South, then two squares East. Write B in the box.

3. Go two squares West, then one square South. Write C in the box.

4. Go one square East, then two squares North, then two squares West.
   Write D in the box.

5. Go two squares West, then two squares North, then three squares East.
   Write E in the box.

Movement and direction

Start facing North each time. Write what you will see after each turn.

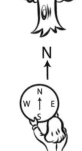

6. $\frac{1}{2}$ turn clockwise → _____

7. $\frac{1}{4}$ turn anti-clockwise → _____

8. $\frac{1}{4}$ turn clockwise → _____

9. $\frac{3}{4}$ turn clockwise → _____

10. $\frac{3}{4}$ turn anti-clockwise → _____

/10

Angles

1. Tick the right angle in each set.

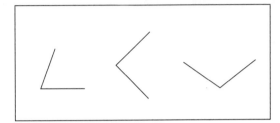 

2. Draw a right angle on this grid.

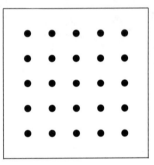

3. How many right angles does a square have?

_____

4. On these shapes, tick each right-angled corner.

5. Draw a circle around the largest angle in this set.

Angles

6. How many right angles make a straight line?

_____

7. Tick each right angle in this shape.

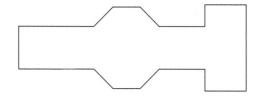

8. Draw a circle around the smallest angle in this set.

9. Put a dot in each right angle.

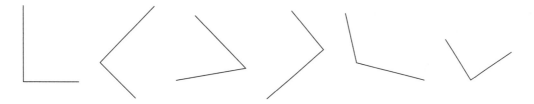

10. Tick the shape that has four right angles.

/10

Measuring length

1. How many centimetres are there in 2 metres?

   _____ cm

2. Write each measurement to the nearest centimetre.

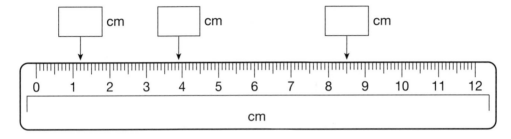

3. Use a ruler to measure the length of this line.

   _____ cm

4. Two sticks are 40 cm and 80 cm in length. What is the total length of the two sticks?

   _____ cm

5. What must be added to each measurement to make 1 metre?

   a) [45 cm + [   ] cm]

   b) [68 cm + [   ] cm]

Measuring length

6. What is the difference in length between these two lines?

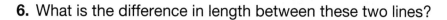

_____ cm

7. Write how many centimetres are in each of these.

a) 5 metres = [ ] cm   **b)** $\frac{1}{2}$ metre = [ ] cm

8. Write each measurement to the nearest $\frac{1}{2}$ cm. One has been done for you.

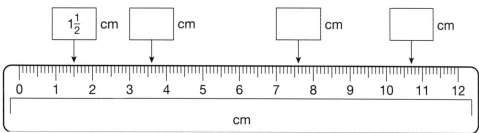

$1\frac{1}{2}$ cm   [ ] cm   [ ] cm   [ ] cm

9. How many metres are in 2 kilometres?

_____ m

10. A piece of string measuring 3 metres is cut in half.

How long is each piece?

_____ cm

/10

Measuring capacity

1. How many millilitres are there in 2 litres?

_____ ml

2. Write how much liquid is in each container.

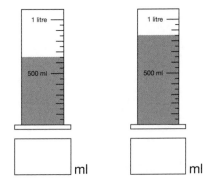

_____ ml   _____ ml

3. How many 50 ml cupfuls will fill a 500 ml jug?

_____

4. What is the total capacity of these two jugs?

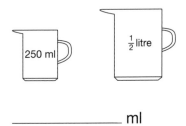

_____ ml

5. What is the difference in capacity between these two jugs?

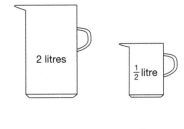

_____ ml

Measuring capacity

6. Write each of these amounts to the nearest litre.

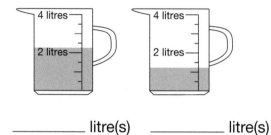

_____ litre(s)   _____ litre(s)

7. How many 200 ml bottles will fill a 1-litre jug?

_____

8. Write how much liquid is in each container.

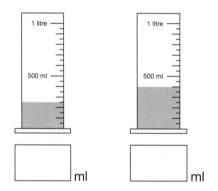

___ ml   ___ ml

9. How many millilitres are equal to three-quarters of a litre?

_____ ml

10. A jug holds 3 litres of water. If half the water is poured out, how much is left?

_____ ml

/10

Measuring weight

1. Write the weight of this parcel in grams.

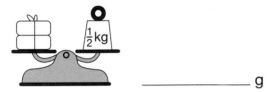

_____ g

2. How many 200 g weights will balance 1 kg?

_____

3. What weight is shown on this scale to the nearest $\frac{1}{2}$ kg?

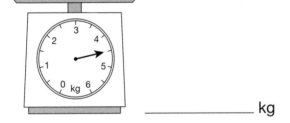

_____ kg

4. What is the difference in weight between these two parcels?

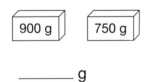

_____ g

5. Complete this.

3 kg = _____ g

Measuring weight

6. What weight is shown on this scale to the nearest kilogram?

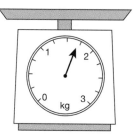

_____ kg

7. How many 50 g weights will balance 1 kg?

_____

8. Write the weight of this parcel in grams.

_____ g

9. What is the total weight of these parcels?

| 800 g | | 700 g |

_____ kg _____ g

10. Complete this.

$$4\frac{1}{2} \text{ kg} = \text{_____ g}$$

/10

Time

1. Write these times.

| : | | : |

2. A bus journey lasts for 40 minutes. If it sets off at 10:30 in the morning, what time does the bus journey end?

_____

3. How many days are in the month of May?

_____ days

4. Write these times.

| : | | : |

5. How many minutes are there between these two times?

☐ minutes

Time

6. How many minutes are in three-quarters of an hour?

_____ minutes

7. Draw the missing hands on these clocks.

| 9:55 | | 6:05 |

8. What time is 20 minutes after 3:15?

_____

9. How many minutes are there between these two times?

[   ] minutes

10. How many days are there in September?

_____ days

/10

Tables, charts and graphs

This pictogram shows the number of children who visited a dentist each day for five days.

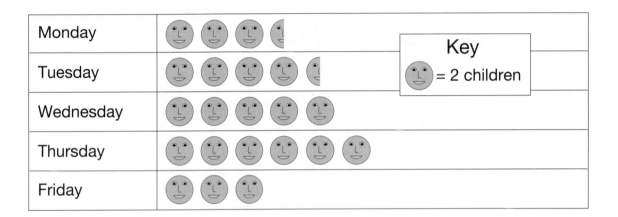

Monday		Key
Tuesday		= 2 children
Wednesday		
Thursday		
Friday		

1. How many children visited the dentist on Thursday?

_____

2. On which day did six children visit the dentist?

_____

3. How many children visited the dentist on Tuesday?

_____

4. How many more children visited the dentist on Wednesday than on Monday?

_____

5. How many children visited the dentist in total?

_____

Tables, charts and graphs

This graph shows the favourite drinks of a group of people in a survey.

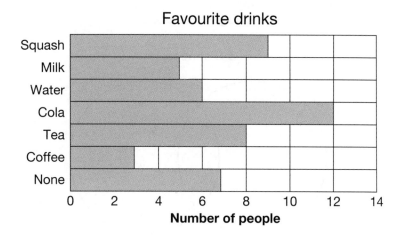

Favourite drinks

Number of people

6. Which drink was the favourite of eight people?

_____

7. How many people chose squash as their favourite drink?

_____

8. How many more people chose cola than coffee as their favourite drink?

_____

9. Which drink was chosen by one fewer person than water as a favourite drink?

_____

10. How many people were in the survey in total?

_____

/10

Venn and Carroll diagrams

1–5. Sort the shapes below. Write the letter of each shape in the correct place on the Venn diagram.

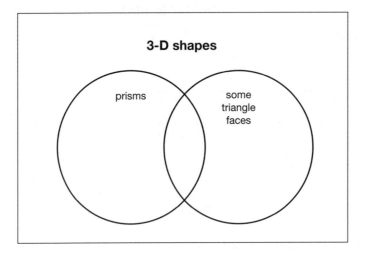

3-D shapes

prisms

some
triangle
faces

A

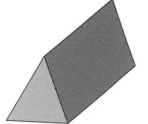

B

C

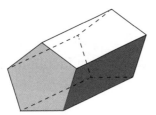

D

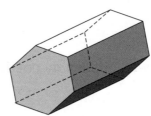

E

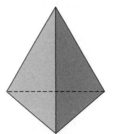

Venn and Carroll diagrams

6–10. Write the names of each fruit in the correct place on the Carroll diagram.

	Can eat the skin	Cannot eat the skin
Has a stone		
Does not have a stone		

pineapple

peach

cherry

strawberry

banana

/10

Fruit code

1. Answer each multiplication. Use the code to change your answer to letters.

A	C	E	G	H	L	M	N	O	P	R	Y
12	15	18	20	21	36	27	30	32	10	24	40

a)

2×5 2×9 5×2 3×4 4×9

_____   _____   _____   _____   _____

b)

5×4 10×1 6×4 6×2 2×9

_____   _____   _____   _____   _____

c)

3×8 6×3 3×5 3×7 4×6 10×4

_____   _____   _____   _____   _____   _____

d)

4×5 3×6 10×3 8×4 8×3 4×3

_____   _____   _____   _____   _____   _____

2. Rearrange the letters in **a)** to **d)** above to spell four fruits. Draw each fruit.

a)

b)

c)

d)

Shape wordsearch

Find all the 2-D and 3-D shapes in this wordsearch.

Words to find:

circle	☐	hexagon	☐	pyramid	☐
cone	☐	kite	☐	rectangle	☐
cube	☐	oval	☐	sphere	☐
cuboid	☐	pentagon	☐	square	☐
cylinder	☐	prism	☐	triangle	☐

b	a	n	k	i	t	e	t	p	r
h	o	o	v	a	l	l	s	y	e
e	l	g	n	a	t	c	e	r	d
x	s	a	e	f	r	r	b	a	n
a	p	t	c	r	i	i	u	m	i
g	h	n	u	m	a	c	c	i	l
o	e	e	b	s	n	u	e	d	y
n	r	p	o	i	g	l	q	m	c
t	e	n	i	r	l	i	n	s	d
r	e	h	d	p	e	c	o	n	e

Progress report

Colour each box in the correct colour to show how many questions you got right.

0–2 = yellow, 3–5 = green, 6–7 = blue, 8–10 = red

This will help you to monitor your progress.

Test 1	Test 2	Test 3	Test 4	Test 5
/10	/10	/10	/10	/10
Date _____	Date _____	Date _____	Date _____	Date _____

Test 6	Test 7	Test 8	Test 9	Test 10
/10	/10	/10	/10	/10
Date _____	Date _____	Date _____	Date _____	Date _____

Test 11	Test 12	Test 13	Test 14	Test 15
				If you did it in less than 10 minutes, colour this red. If you took longer, colour this blue.
/10	/10	/10	/10	
Date _____	Date _____	Date _____	Date _____	Date _____

Test 16	Test 17	Test 18	Test 19	Test 20
If you did it in less than 10 minutes, colour this red. If you took longer, colour this blue.				
	/10	/10	/10	/10
Date _____	Date _____	Date _____	Date _____	Date _____

Test 21	Test 22	Test 23	Test 24	Test 25
/10	/10	/10	/10	/10
Date _____	Date _____	Date _____	Date _____	Date _____

Test 26	Test 27	Test 28	Test 29	Test 30
			If you complete the puzzle, then colour this red.	If you complete the wordsearch, then colour this red.
/10	/10	/10		
Date _____	Date _____	Date _____	Date _____	Date _____